ASSESSING YOUR CHILD'S PROGRESS

Testing and assessment in the National Curriculum

Pupils between the ages of 7 and 11 (Years 3–6) cover Key Stage 2 of the National Curriculum. In May of their final year of Key Stage 2 (Year 6) all pupils take written National Tests (commonly known as SATs) in the three most important subjects: English, Mathematics and Science. Your child may already have taken some National Tests at the end of Key Stage 1 (Year 2). These will have been in number, shape and space, reading, writing, handwriting and spelling.

At the end of Key Stage 1, your child will have been awarded a National Curriculum level for each subject tested. When your child eventually takes the Key Stage 2 tests, he or she again will be awarded a level. On average, pupils are expected to advance one level for every two years they are at school. The target for pupils at the end of Key Stage 1 is Level 2. By the end of Key Stage 2, four years later, the target is Level 4. The table below will show you how your child should progress.

	7 years	11 years		
Level 6		▧	▧	Exceptional performance
Level 5		▨	▨	Exceeded targets for age group
Level 4	▧	▤	▤	Achieved targets for age group
Level 3	▨	☐		
Level 2	▤	☐	☐	Working towards targets for age group
Level 1	☐	☐		

Assessing your child's progress throughout Key Stage 2 of the National Curriculum

The aim of the Letts Assessment books is to help you monitor your child's progress in English, Mathematics and Science throughout Key Stage 2. There are four books for each subject – one for each year, starting with 7–8 year olds. The questions in the books become progressively harder with each year, so that for 10–11 year olds, the questions will be at a level similar to the Key Stage 2 National Tests.

After completing a book, your child will have a score which you will be able to interpret using the progress indicator provided. This will give you a guide to the level at which your child is working.

ASSESSING YOUR CHILD'S PROGRESS

Using this book to assess your child's progress in Mathematics

This book is for 10–11 year olds (Year 6). It contains four basic features:

Questions: 40 questions, arranged in order of level of difficulty as follows:
                    10 at Level 3 (pages 1–6)
                    15 at Level 4 (pages 7–20)
                    15 at Level 5 (pages 21–34)

Answers: showing acceptable responses and marks

Note to Parent: giving advice on what your child should be doing and how to help

Progress Chart: showing you how to interpret your child's marks to arrive at a level

- Your child should not attempt to do all the questions in the book in one go. Try setting ten questions at a time. If your child does not understand a question, you might want to explain it. Although the questions in this book are not meant to constitute a formal test, you should encourage your child to answer as many as possible without help. Read the questions to your child if you think it will help.

- When your child has completed the questions, turn to the Answer section at the back of the book. Using the recommended answers, award your child the appropriate mark or marks for each question. In the margin of each question page, there are small boxes. These are divided in half with the marks available for that question at the bottom, and a blank at the top for you to fill in your child's score.

- Collate your child's marks on the grid on page 46. Then add them up. Once you have the total, turn to page 35 at the front of the Answer section and look at the Progress Chart to determine your child's level.

- Work through the answers with your child, using the Note to Parent to help give advice, correct mistakes and explain problems.

Equipment your child will need for this book

The following equipment may be needed for answering these questions:

- a pen, pencil, rubber and coloured pencils

- a ruler (30 cm plastic ruler is most suitable)

- a calculator. An inexpensive four-function calculator is all that is required. Do not let your child use a scientific calculator which has too many complicated functions

- a mirror. This is useful for symmetry questions

- angle measurer. The angle measurer is probably easier to use than the protractor, particularly for angles greater than 180°

- tracing paper. This is useful for rotational symmetry questions

Some questions in this book ban the use of a calculator.

The following symbol is used:

1 Miss Smith's class are setting out the chairs in the hall. There are 90 small chairs to be placed in 10 equal rows.

a
How many chairs will there be in each row?

....

There are 75 big chairs which are arranged in rows with 15 chairs in each row.

b
How many rows will there be?

....

1

Q1a

1

Q1b

2

| Grapefruit 40p | Pears 25p | Peaches 18p | Baking potatoes 15p |

Sam went shopping for his mother.

Fill in Sam's bill.

5

Q2

```
2 grapefruit      ....................................
3 pears           ....................................
2 peaches         ....................................
4 potatoes        ....................................
                  - - - - - - - - - - - - - - - - - -
Total
                  - - - - - - - - - - - - - - - - - -
```

3 Look at these shapes drawn on a square grid.

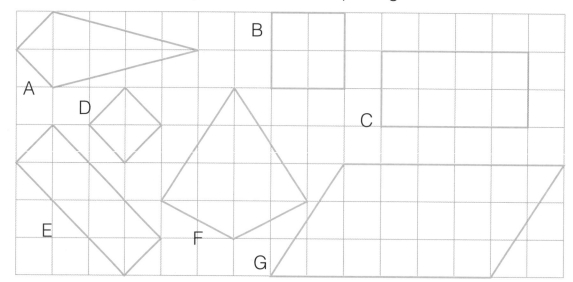

a

7

Q3a

Fill in the table which sorts the shapes into groups. Tick ✓ the box if the description fits.

Shape	All sides equal	Opposite sides parallel	All angles right angles
A			
B			
C			
D			
E			
F			
G			

b

2

Q3b

Finish the following sentences.

Shapes A and F are called ....

Shape G is called a ....

2

4   Some children measured the heights of trees in a wood. The pictogram below shows part of the results.

Height   **Number of trees**   represents 5 trees

up to 10 m

between 10 m
and 20 m

a | How many trees were up to 10 metres tall? |

....

1

Q4a

b | How many trees were between 10 and 20 metres tall? |

....

1

Q4b

There were 32 trees between 20 and 30 metres tall.

c | Draw this as a pictogram in the box below. |

| between 20 m
and 30 m |

1

Q4c

5   Class 6 are going to the pantomime. Miss Brown and some parents are taking them by car. There are 29 children.

| If each car has room for three children, how many cars will be needed for all the children to arrive at the same time? |

1

Q5

....

6 Jenny saved 20p each week.

a | Finish the table showing how much she had each week.

Week	1	2	3	4	5	6	7	8	9
Total saved	20p	40p	60p	80p	£1				

b | How much money would Jenny have saved after 15 weeks?

....

c | If Jenny had saved 30p a week, how much would she have saved over five weeks?

....

7 | Link the clues to the numbers. One has been done for you.

a I am less than 3 × 5
I am more than 5 × 2

19

b I am odd
I am less than 5 × 5
I am more than 8 × 2

14

c I am more than 5 × 5
I am less than 10 × 3

16

d I am even
I am less than 4 × 5
I am more than 7 × 2

27

8 In an end of year spelling test, the following rewards were offered:

Number of correct words	House points
10 or more	1
20 or more	2
30 or more	3
40 or more	4

a Marie had 33 correct words. How many house points does she earn?

1
Q8a

b Darren got 19 words correct and thinks he should have two house points. Why is he wrong?

1
Q8b

c John received two house points. How many words did he get right? Give all the possible answers.

1
Q8c

9 The clock in the classroom is showing the time. It is five minutes to three (5 to 3).

a Write this time as a digital clock or watch would show it.

1
Q9a

The children will go home 25 minutes later.

b Write this time in words and in figures.

1
Q9b

10 Here are some drawings of solid shapes.

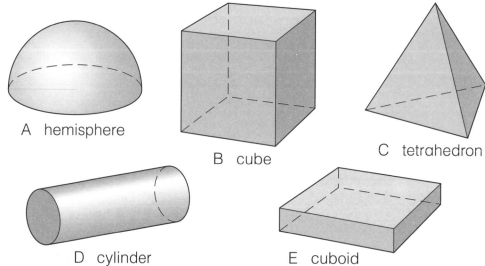

A   hemisphere

B   cube

C   tetrahedron

D   cylinder

E   cuboid

List the shapes that have:

a   at least one face that is a circle;

....

b   no curved faces;

....

c   every face a square;

....

d   one or more right angles;

....

e   some faces that are rectangles;

....

f   one or more curved faces.

....

11 Class 6 are doing some work on their village.
Here is a sketch map showing important buildings and the distances in metres between them.

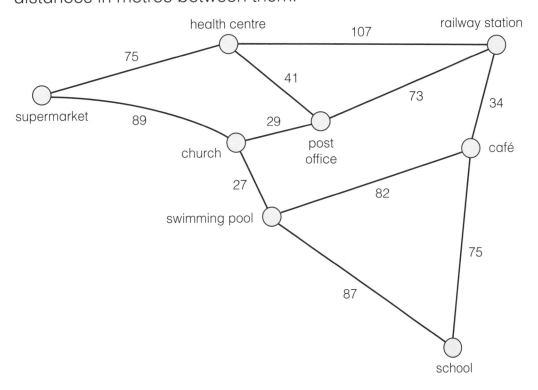

a

How far is it from the post office to:

the railway station?...

the swimming pool?...

the café?...

the supermarket?...

4

Q11a

b

Find the shortest distance from the post office to the school.

1

Q11b

....

12 Richard has made a triangle
with elastic bands on a
nailboard. This is shape A.

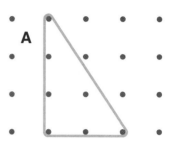

He then makes six other shapes.

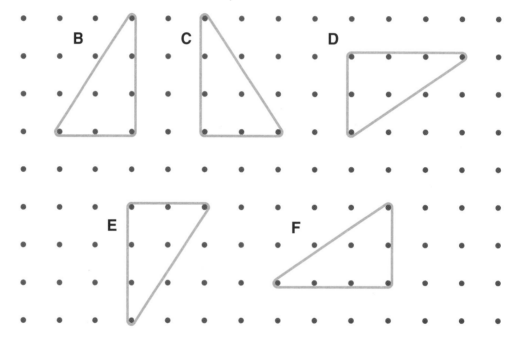

Fill in the table below. Tick ✓ the box if the description fits.

Shape	Is a reflection of shape A	Is a rotation of shape A	is neither a reflection or a rotation
B			
C			
D			
E			
F			

5

Q12

13 Tom is a milkman. Here is a list of the deliveries he makes in Slater Road each day from Monday to Saturday.

House number	Pints daily
56	6
57	3
59	7
60	9
61	2
62	5
63	4
64	10
NO SUNDAY DELIVERY	

a How many pints of milk does he deliver in one day?

1

Q13a

b How many pints is this in one week?

1

Q13b

One week, number 62 cancelled their milk for two days.

c How much milk did they have that week?

1

Q13c

d If milk costs 37p per pint, how much does number 57 pay in one week?

1

Q13d

14 Here is a table of information about a short journey made by a small aircraft.

Time (in minutes)	Height (in metres)
0	0
1	0
2	500
3	1000
4	1500
5	2000
6	2000
7	2000
8	2000
9	1500
10	1000
11	500
12	0

a Finish the line graph by plotting the last four values and connecting the crosses.

1

Q14a

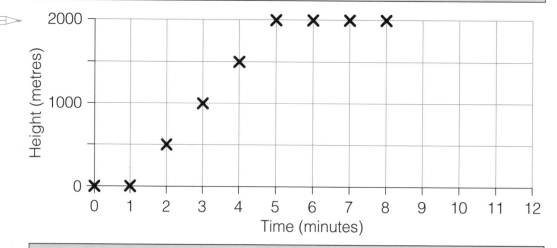

b What was the height of the aircraft after $4\frac{1}{2}$ minutes?

1

Q14b

c

What was the aircraft doing:

between 0 and 5 minutes into its flight?

....

between 5 and 8 minutes into its flight?

....

between 9 and 12 minutes into its flight?

....

3

Q14c

15   Sally and Jane are playing a "funny face" card game.
       Sally's cards are shown below.

Jane chooses one of Sally's cards without seeing the picture.

Tick ✓ **one** box for each question below to show how likely it
is that the face on the card Jane chose will have:

4

Q15

		Impossible	Unlikely	Even chance	Likely	Certain
a	a round head;	☐	☐	☐	☐	☐
b	straight hair;	☐	☐	☐	☐	☐
c	curly hair;	☐	☐	☐	☐	☐
d	four eyes.	☐	☐	☐	☐	☐

5

Q16

16 Match these addition and subtraction questions to their correct answers. The first one has been done for you.

1.39 + 3.21	9.11
3.21 − 1.10	4.60
6.01 + 3.10	9.99
9.01 − 8.75	2.11
6.88 − 5.19	0.26
8.80 + 1.19	1.69

17 David and Emma used some fractions cards in their maths work.

$\frac{1}{10}$	$\frac{1}{3}$	$\frac{1}{20}$	$\frac{2}{8}$	$\frac{6}{10}$
$\frac{1}{100}$	$\frac{60}{100}$	$\frac{25}{50}$	$\frac{3}{5}$	$\frac{4}{8}$

They decided to sort their fractions cards into three groups.

10

Q17

Sort their cards into three groups by filling in the boxes.

Less than a half	A half	More than a half

18 Class 5 are weighing objects. They use a variety of measuring instruments and record the mass of each object. The values are shown below.

Object	1	2	3	4	5	6
Mass	15 kg	225 g	5.5 kg	1 kg	550 g	1500 g

Here are six pictures of the scales which gave these readings:

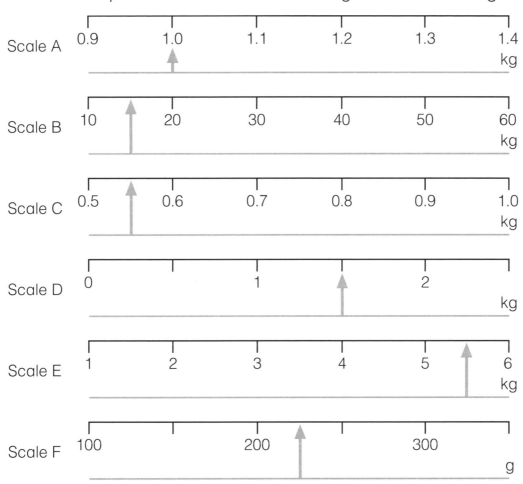

Fill in the correct object number underneath each scale letter in the table below.

Scale	A	B	C	D	E	F
Object						

19

PRICE LIST

Apples per $\frac{1}{2}$ kg	26p
Pears per $\frac{1}{2}$ kg	38p
Bananas per $\frac{1}{2}$ kg	41p
Potatoes per bag	19p
Carrots per kg	22p
Tomatoes per kg	37p

a

3

Q19a

Find the cost of:

 $1\frac{1}{2}$ kg apples ....

1 kg pears ....

4 bags potatoes ....

b

4

Q19b

Find the total cost of these two orders and then calculate the change given.

Order 1

1 kg bananas ....

1 bag potatoes ....

1 kg tomatoes ....

Total ....

Change from £2 ....

Order 2

2 kg carrots ....

$\frac{1}{2}$ kg pears ....

2 kg apples ....

Total ....

Change from £5 ....

20 Some hexagons are painted on the school yard. They have sides all 1 m long.

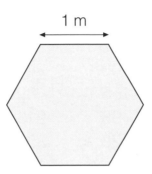

1 m

a

What is the perimeter of one hexagon?

 ....

A path of hexagons is painted like the one shown below:

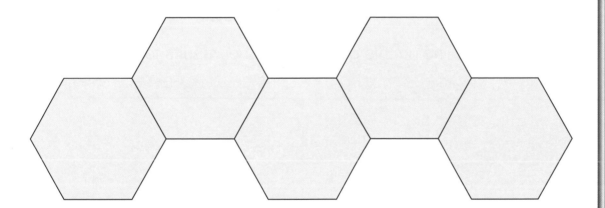

b

What is the perimeter of the path?

....

21 Hannah works at the entrance to a safari park. She counts the number of cars that drive through each day. Here are her results for June.

86	67	247	106	217
220	103	244	239	94
241	155	89	152	101
151	98	213	132	186
89	123	227	92	209
183	232	157	148	95

a

5

Q21a

Fill in this frequency table.

Number of cars	Tally	Frequency
51 to 100		
101 to 150		
151 to 200		
201 to 250		
Total		

The blue line on this graph shows her results for August.

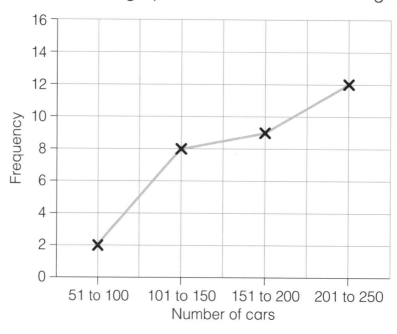

b

Draw her results for June on the graph.

c

Which month was the busiest?

✏ ....

22

What fraction of each grid has been coloured?

a

b

✏ ....   ✏ ....

c

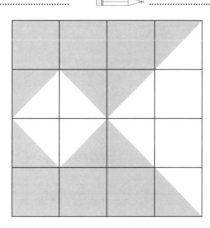

✏ ....

Letts

Q23a

Q23b

Q23c

Q23d

23 Lynsey is going swimming. The pool is 25 m long. Lynsey swims eight lengths.

a | How far does Lynsey swim?

The water temperature is 30°C. Lynsey wants to know what this is in °F. She works this out by:

1   multiplying by 9
2   dividing by 5
3   adding 32

b | Work out 30×9.

c | Divide your answer to question **b** by 5.

d | Add 32 to your answer to question **c**.

24 This table shows how fractions can be shown on a grid.

Fraction	Point
$\frac{1}{2}$	(1,2)
$\frac{2}{4}$	(2,4)
$\frac{4}{8}$	(4,8)

a

Plot the points (2,4), (4,8) and (1,2) on the grid below and join them with a straight line.

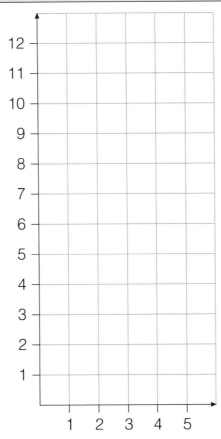

$\frac{2}{4}$ and $\frac{4}{8}$ are fractions equal to $\frac{1}{2}$. All three fractions are in a straight line on the graph.

b

Write down another fraction equal to $\frac{1}{2}$.

....

$\frac{2}{6}$ and $\frac{4}{12}$ are fractions equal to $\frac{1}{3}$.

c

Draw another straight line with these fractions on the grid.
Use it to write another fraction equal to $\frac{1}{3}$.

....

25 Peter wants to make 240 buns for his school's summer fair.
The recipe book says to make 16 buns you need:

2 eggs
50 g flour
50 g margarine
50 g sugar

a What will Peter need to make 240 buns?

5

Q25a

.... eggs

.... flour

.... margarine

.... sugar

Peter has a $1\frac{1}{2}$ kg bag of flour.

b Is this enough to make 240 buns?

1

Q25b

....

The buns have to be cooked for 15 minutes.

c If he puts some buns in the oven at 10 to 3, what time should he take them out?

1

Q25c

....

26 This table shows the number of spectators at Little Puddington Football Club's home matches so far this season.

Week	Attendance
1	914
2	894
3	1102
4	983
5	1211
6	1532

a Which week's match drew the largest crowd?

1

Q26a

b What was the total attendance over the first six weeks of the season?

1

Q26b

c What was the mean weekly attendance?

1

Q26c

The admission to each match was £3 a ticket.

d How much was collected in admission charges so far this season?

1

Q26d

27 This chart shows the mean amount of pocket money that children are given at different ages.

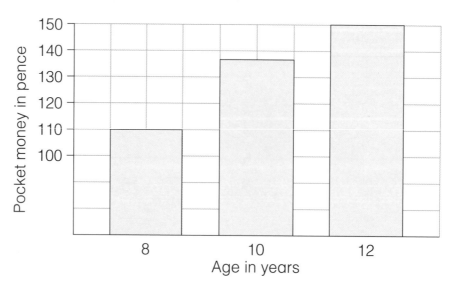

Christine says that 12 year-olds get twice as much as 8 year-olds.

a

Is she right?

✏️ ....

b

Explain why.

✏️ ....

....

28 In the toy shop's sale, everything is reduced by $\frac{1}{5}$.

What is the price in the sale of a microscope which used to cost £14.99?

✏️ ....

....

1
Q27a

1
Q27b

2
Q28

29   Look at this thermometer.
It measures temperature
in °C (degrees Celsius).

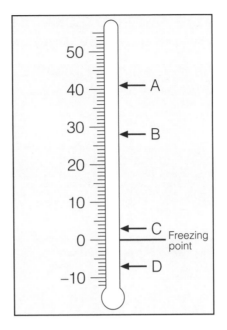

a   How many degrees does one small division represent?

1

Q29a

b   What temperature is shown at:

1

Q29b

A .... B .... C .... D ....

c   What would the temperature be if it rose by 9°C from **C**?

1

Q29c

d   What would the temperature be if it fell by 11°C from **C**?

1

Q29d

e   What is the lowest temperature measured on this thermometer?

1

Q29e

30 Tim and Kerry are making kites out of cloth. They use wood for the diagonal frames. First, they draw some kites to scale on centimetre squared paper.

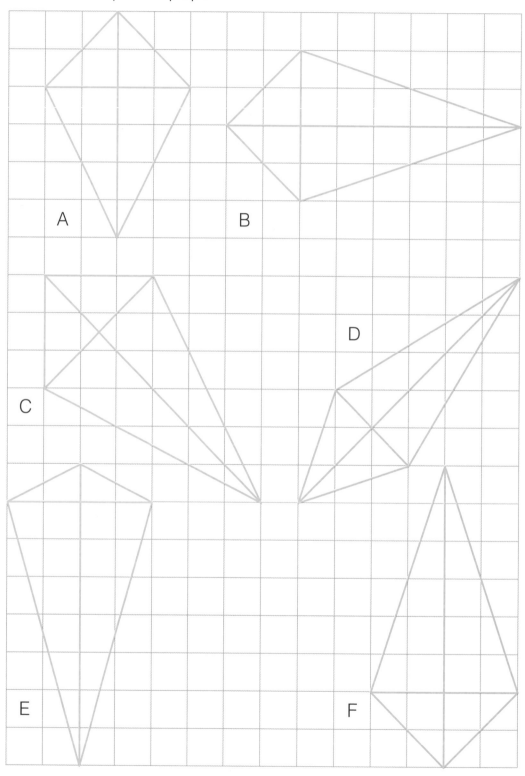

a

Measure the diagonals to the nearest 0.5 cm and fill in the table.

6
Q30a

Kite	Length diagonal	Width diagonal
A		
B		
C		
D		
E		
F		

b

Which kites are congruent?

1
Q30b

....

c

Which kite will need the most cloth to make?

1
Q30c

....

d

At what angle do all the diagonals cross each other?

1
Q30d

....

e

Which diagonal represents the line of symmetry for each kite?

1
Q30e

....

31 Alex goes to Scarborough on holiday. This graph shows the height of the tide each day

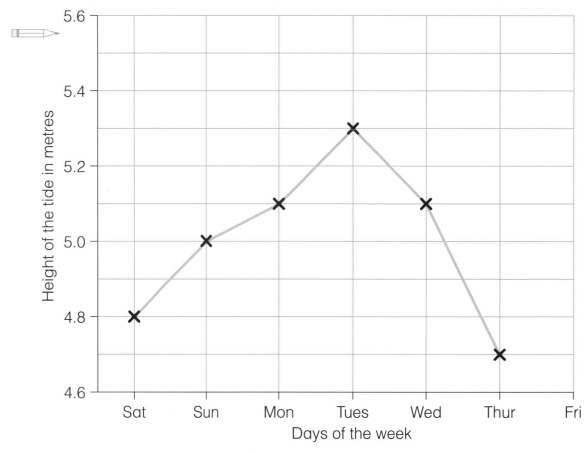

a How high was the tide on Sunday?

Friday's high tide was 4.9 metres.

b Draw in Friday's high tide on the graph.

c Which day had the highest tide?

1
Q31a

1
Q31b

1
Q31c

d

On which two days was the tide the same height?

e

Work out the range of the heights of the tides.

32

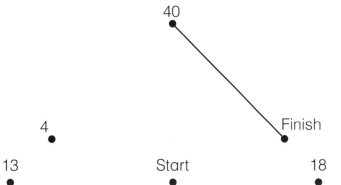

Join the dots in this order:

from the start go to a multiple of 6;
then to a factor of 20;
then to the square of 3;
then to a prime number;
then back to the start;
then to a multiple of 8;
then to the square root of 16;
then to the finish.

33 Katie has a guinea pig. Her mum makes a pen for it with wire netting. The pen is a rectangle.

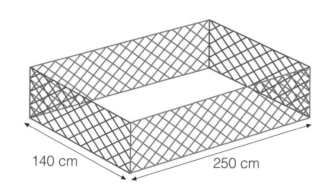

140 cm   250 cm

a What length of wire netting does Katie's mum need?

1

Q33a

Wire is sold in whole metres only.

b How many metres should she buy?

1

Q33b

A fully grown guinea pig is about 12 inches long.

c Roughly how many centimetres is this?

1

Q33c

34 Here are some prices of petrol at local garages.

a How much will 30 litres of the cheapest petrol cost?

1

Q34a

Peter bought 25 litres of petrol. It cost him £13.35.

b

Which petrol did he buy?

✏️ ....

c

How much would he have paid for 20 litres of Maxi petrol?

✏️ ....

35

Shelford Leisure Centre
E N T R Y   F E E S
Badminton **£4.50**   Squash **£2.50**   Aerobics **£1.60**   Spectators **40p**

Tim plays badminton twice a week and squash once a week.

a

How much does Tim spend at the leisure centre in one month?

✏️ ....

Tim's grandad goes to watch him play squash and goes to aerobics once a week. As an OAP, his entry fees are half price.

b

How much does Tim's grandad pay each week?

✏️ ....

On a Sunday all prices are reduced by 10%.

c

What are the new prices?

✏️ Badminton ....   Squash ....

Aerobics ....   Spectators ....

MARKS

36 Below are five shapes each made from 1 cm squares. Some of the shapes will fold up to make an open box.

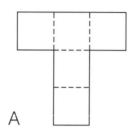
A

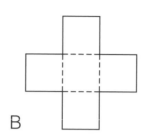
B

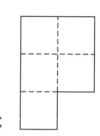
C

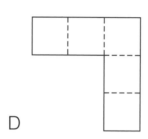
D

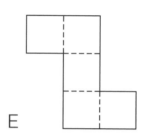
E

a

Fill in the perimeter of each shape in the table.

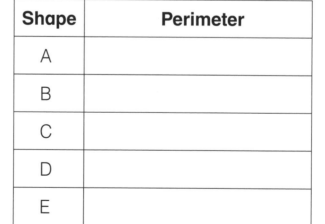

Shape	Perimeter
A	
B	
C	
D	
E	

5

Q36a

b

Which shapes will fold to make an open box?

1

Q36b

37 Sarah is using pipe cleaners to make 3-D shapes. She builds two shapes, a cuboid and a prism.

cuboid

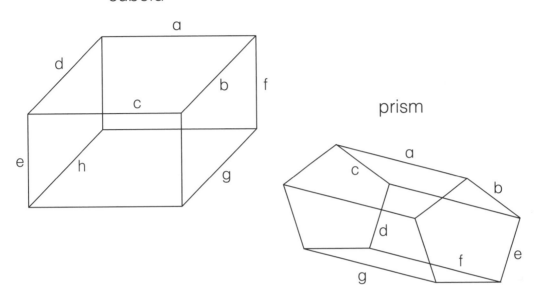

prism

The drawings show some edges marked with letters.

a

Fill in the tables below about parallel edges.

6

Q37a

Cuboid

Edge	Parallel to
a	
b	
f	

Prism

Edge	Parallel to
a	
b	
e	

b

Which **two** plane shapes are the faces of the prism?

1

Q37b

Letts

MARKS

38 This table shows the number of people living in four towns.

Town	Population
Johnstown	230
Fourpost	620
Staley	358
Carton	434

a How many more people live at Fourpost than Carton?

1

Q38a

One fifth of Johnstown's population live in houses with three bedrooms.

b How many people is that?

1

Q38b

Three quarters of Fourpost's population have a garage.

c How many people have garages?

1

Q38c

Half of Staley's population and half of Carton's people shop at a nearby superstore.

d How many people went to the superstore from these two towns?

1

Q38d

39 Lathe Road Primary School band need some new recorders.
These are prices in the catalogue:

Descant Recorders   £2.85 each

Treble Recorders   £7.50 each

a | How much would five treble recorders cost?

1

Q39a

....

The band need 11 descant recorders

b | How much will these cost?

1

Q39b

....

c | What is the difference in cost between the five treble
recorders and the 11 descant recorders?

1

Q39c

....

The cost of treble recorders is reduced by 10%.

d | How much does one treble recorder cost now?

1

Q39d

....

33

40   The diagram shows a five-sided shape. The length of each side is shown by a letter.

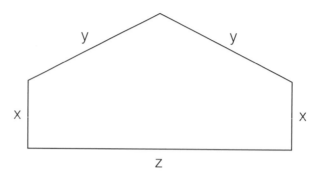

a

1

Q40a

Write down a formula for the perimeter of the shape.

....

b

1

Q40b

If x = 2 cm, y = 4 cm and z = 6 cm,
calculate the actual perimeter of the shape.

....

MARKING YOUR CHILD'S ANSWERS

- The answers given here are correct answers. They are the answers the question-setter expects. When marking your child's work, you must look at his or her answers and judge whether they deserve credit. Award the mark if the answer deserves credit.

- At this age, your child's spelling may show a number of errors. Do not mark any answer wrong because the words are misspelt. Read the word aloud and if it sounds correct award the mark. For example, 'ekwul' would be acceptable for 'equal'.

- When you go through the questions with your child, try to be positive. Look for good things that have been done in addition to showing where errors have been made.

- Enter your child's marks on the grid on page 46, and then refer to the chart below to determine your child's level.

Progress Chart

Total marks scored	Progress made	Suggested action
40 or below	Your child is still working within Level 3.	Analyse errors and mistakes especially in the first ten questions. Make sure your child knows the 2, 5 and 10 times table and can recognise shapes and measure lines.
41–80	Your child is working with growing confidence within Level 4.	Check your child's competence with addition and subtraction of decimals to two places; with the reflection and rotation of shapes; and his or her understanding of median and mode.
81–115	Your child is confident with the Level 4 work presented here.	Look at any errors made in questions 10 to 25, and perhaps beyond, and try to identify the mistakes made. Use the Note to Parent to help.
116–140	Your child is working with growing confidence at Level 5.	Practise working with decimals to two decimal places, and multiplying and dividing whole numbers without a calculator.
141 or above	Your child is confident with the Level 5 work presented here.	A very good score. The skills of interpreting graphs and diagrams, using simple algebra and recognising the symmetries of different shapes are necessary at this Level and need to be practised.

- A child at the end of Year 6 (10–11 year olds) should be, of the above statements, at about the third statement.

1 a 9   *1 mark*
     b 5   *1 mark*

Note to Parent

Your child ought to be able to work these questions out by division without adding or subtracting to find the numbers.

Total 2 marks

2 2 grapefruit = 80p, 3 pears = 75p, 2 peaches = 36p, 4 baking potatoes = 60p
    Total = £2.51
    Award one mark for each correct answer. Award a mark for the correct totalling of incorrect answers   *5 marks*

Note to Parent

If the answer for the total is given in pence, ask your child to change it into pounds.

Total 5 marks

3 a

Shape	All sides equal	Opposite sides parallel	All angles right angles
A			
B	✓	✓	✓
C		✓	✓
D	✓	✓	✓
E		✓	✓
F			
G		✓	

    Award one mark for each correctly identified shape   *7 marks*
    b A and F are kites   *1 mark*
       G is a parallelogram   *1 mark*

Note to Parent

This question requires a developing knowledge of shape attributes and children need to discuss the meaning of terms such as parallel, opposite and vertical. A useful extension activity is to play a shape game with your child, in which you specify specific criteria for a shape to be drawn, for example draw a four-sided shape with three right angles.

Total 9 marks

4 a 25   *1 mark*
     b 43 or 44   *1 mark*
     c There should be six complete trees and one which is less than half a tree   *1 mark*

Note to Parent

For part **b**, your child should recognise that there is more than half a tree, but less than a full tree, hence either 43 or 44 trees is acceptable. For part **c** your child should draw less than half a tree.

Total 3 marks

5   10 cars   *1 mark*
       (29 ÷ 3 = 9 remainder 2)

Note to Parent

These sort of questions require your child to recognise that only whole number answers are acceptable and that the answer is the next whole number, that is round up not down.

Total 1 mark

6   a

6	7	8	9
£1.20	£1.40	£1.60	£1.80

1 mark
      b   £3.00   *1 mark*
      c   £1.50   *1 mark*

Note to Parent

Once your child has recognised the 20p jumping pattern, he or she should be able to apply the same rule to part **b**. Note the need to change from pence into pounds.

Total 3 marks

7   b   19
      c   27
      d   16   *1 mark each*

Note to Parent

It might help to write down the solutions to the clues rather than memorise them. This kind of activity is a good way to practise mental arithmetic and it is fairly easy to think up clues.

Total 3 marks

8   a   3   *1 mark*
      b   Although he was very close to the '20 or more' category, he is still in
          the '10 or more' one and so only deserves one house point   *1 mark*
      c   20, 21, 22, 23, 24, 25, 26, 27, 28, 29   *1 mark*

Note to Parent

Children must study the table carefully and not assume that rounding up should be used here.

Total 3 marks

9   a   Either 2:55 or 14:55   *1 mark*
      b   twenty past three (20 past 3) or 15:20 or 3:20   *1 mark*

Note to Parent

Children find the topic of time difficult, particularly the words 'past' and 'to'. They need to be able to cope with addition and subtraction of time and become familiar with the 24 hour clock. Practise more questions using such things as timers on cookers or reading bus and train timetables. Remember that calculators will not usually help with the addition or subtraction of time intervals.

Total 2 marks

10   *Your child may use names or letters*

a	A, D	*1 mark*
b	B, C, E	*1 mark*
c	B	*1 mark*
d	B, E	*1 mark*
e	E	*1 mark*
f	A, D	*1 mark*

Note to Parent

Let your child practise naming shapes and describing them around the house. Note the difference between a cube where all faces are square, and a cuboid where some or all faces are rectangles.

Total 6 marks

11   a   73 m   *1 mark*

56 m   *1 mark*

107 m   *1 mark*

Either 41 m + 75 m = 116 m   or 29 m + 89 m = 118 m   *1 mark*

   b   143 m   *1 mark*

Note to Parent

Similar problems to this are easily created and give practice in addition (or with different questions, such as 'How much further…?' in subtraction).

Total 5 marks

12

Shape	Is a reflection of shape A	Is a rotation of shape A	Is neither a reflection or a rotation
B	✓		
C			✓
D		✓	
E	✓		
F		✓	

Award one mark for each correctly identified shape   *5 marks*

Note to Parent

Children's work on reflective symmetry (or line symmetry as it is also called) is best developed practically with the help of a small mirror. Rotational symmetry can also be shown practically with the aid of tracing paper and pins. Trace the outline of the shape, pin the tracing paper (usually at a shape corner) and rotate the paper (usually through one or more right angles).

Total 5 marks

13   a   46   *1 mark*

   b   276   *1 mark*

   c   20 pints   *1 mark*

   d   £6.66   *1 mark*

Note to Parent

The question clearly states that a week in this case is six days not seven.

Total 4 marks

14 a

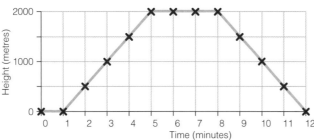

| | 1 mark |

b   1750 m   1 mark

c   gaining height or taking off   1 mark
    flying at a level height   1 mark
    descending or landing   1 mark

Note to Parent

A line graph is distinct in that the information on the axes is written on the line of the squared paper rather than in boxes. Line graphs are useful because once they are drawn you can gain new information by calculating the intermediate value. Children should be able to do this.

Total 5 marks

15 a   even chance   1 mark
     b   likely   1 mark
     c   unlikely   1 mark
     d   impossible   1 mark

Note to Parent

For each question there are eight cards to be considered. 'Impossible' means that there are no possible answers out of the eight. 'Unlikely' means that there are between one and three possible answers out of eight. 'Even chance' means that there are four possible answers. 'Likely' means that there are between five and seven possible answers. 'Certain' means that all eight are possible.

Total 4 marks

16 $3·21 − 1·10 = 2·11$ 1 mark
         $6·01 + 3·10 = 9·11$ 1 mark
         $9·01 − 8·75 = 0·26$ 1 mark
         $6·88 − 5·19 = 1·69$ 1 mark
         $8·80 + 1·19 = 9·99$ 1 mark

Note to Parent

Try to get your child to work the sums out mentally and then check using a calculator.

Total 5 marks

17   Less than a half: $\frac{1}{10}$, $\frac{1}{3}$, $\frac{1}{20}$, $\frac{2}{8}$, $\frac{1}{100}$
         A half: $\frac{25}{50}$, $\frac{4}{8}$
         More than a half: $\frac{3}{5}$, $\frac{6}{10}$, $\frac{60}{100}$
         Award one mark for each fraction correctly grouped   10 marks

Note to Parent

To help your child understand the concept of a fraction, she or he may wish to make some simple fractions cards by folding a piece of paper to find a half, a quarter, an eighth etc.

Total 10 marks

18

Scale	A	B	C	D	E	F
Object	4	1	5	6	3	2

Award one mark for each correct object   *6 marks*

Note to Parent

Children are required to read off scales and understand the value of metric units of mass (weight). Understanding of decimals is also central to this question. Practical work on a range of measuring instruments (tape measures, kitchen and bathroom scales etc.) is necessary before a thorough understanding can be achieved with most children.

Total 6 marks

19 a   78p   *1 mark*
             76p   *1 mark*
             76p   *1 mark*
       b   Order 1, total cost = £1.38, change = 62p   *2 marks*
             Order 2, total cost = £1.86, change = £3.14 *2 marks*
             Award one mark for total cost and one mark for change

Note to Parent

To complete this activity, your child must realise that ½ kg + ½ kg = 1 kg.

Total 7 marks

20 a   The perimeter of one hexagon is 1 m × 6 = 6 m   *1 mark*
       b   The perimeter of the path is 22 m   *1 mark*

Note to Parent

Perimeter is the sum of the lengths of the edges or sides of a shape – here it is a regular shape as all the sides are 1 metre long. The question develops the idea of perimeter to the distance around the outer boundary of a complex shape.

Total 2 marks

21 a   51 to 100 =   8
                101 to 150 =   6
                151 to 200 =   6
                201 to 250 = 10
                     Total = 30
             Award one mark for each correct row and one mark for the correct total   *5 marks*
       b

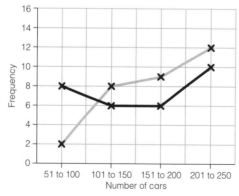

                                                           1 mark
       c   August   *1 mark*
             Total 7 marks

22 a   ½   *1 mark*
       b   ¼   *1 mark*
       c   ⅝   *1 mark*

Note to Parent

In this question, your child should work out what fraction of the shapes have been coloured. The easiest way is for your child to count the shaded squares and half squares.

Total 3 marks

23 a   200 m   *1 mark*
       b   270   *1 mark*
       c   54   *1 mark*
       d   86   *1 mark*

Note to Parent

This question tests your child's ability to manipulate whole numbers without the use of a calculator.

Total 4 marks

24

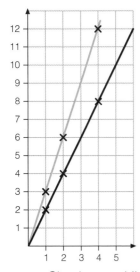

       a   Check your child's line with the black line shown on the graph above   *1 mark*
       b   ⅜ or ⁵⁄₁₀   *1 mark*
       c   Check your child's line with the blue line on the graph above
           ⅔   *1 mark*

Note to Parent

The first figure in the co-ordinate is the distance across the page; the second figure is the distance up. All points on a particular line will give equivalent (equal) fractions.

Total 3 marks

25 a   240 ÷ 16 = 15 so Peter needs:
           15 × 2 = 30 eggs
           15 × 50 = 750 g of flour, margarine and sugar.
           Award one mark for calculating 15 and one mark for each correct quantity   *5 marks*
       b   1½ kg = 1500 g so yes, he has enough   *1 mark*
       c   five past three, or 5 past 3, or 3:05 or 15:05   *1 mark*
                                                         Total 7 marks

26 a week 6   *1 mark*
        b 6636   *1 mark*
        c 1106   *1 mark*
        d £19908   *1 mark*

Note to Parent

Your child may use a calculator for this activity, but encourage him or her to think carefully about the most appropriate operations to use. The 'mean' is the total attendance divided by the number of weeks.

Total 4 marks

27 a No   *1 mark*
        b Eight year-olds get 110p. Twice as much would be 220p.
           Twelve year-olds only get 150p   *1 mark*

Note to Parent

This is a misleading chart. Looking at the heights of the bars, it appears that twelve year-olds do get twice as much as eight year-olds. This is achieved by not starting the vertical axis at zero.

Total 2 marks

28 £14.99 ÷ 5 = £3.00 to the nearest penny   *1 mark*
        £14.99 – £3 = £11.99   *1 mark*

Note to Parent

Your child needs to recognise that finding a fifth is the same as dividing by five.

Total 2 marks

29 a 1°C   *1 mark*
        b A 41°C, B 28°C, C 3°C, D –7°C   *1 mark*
        c 12°C   *1 mark*
        d –8°C   *1 mark*
        e –12°C   *1 mark*

Note to Parent

Your child will need to understand negative numbers and the fact that below freezing point the degrees become minus numbers.

Total 5 marks

30 a

Kite	Length diagonal	Width diagonal
A	6 cm	4 cm
B	8 cm	4 cm
C	8.5 cm	4 cm
D	8.5 cm	3 cm
E	8 cm	4 cm
F	8 cm	4 cm

Award one mark for each correctly measured pair of diagonals   *6 marks*

b	kites B and F are congruent (exactly alike)		*1 mark*
c	kite C will require the most cloth to make as both diagonals have the largest values and therefore the kite will have the largest surface area		*1 mark*
d	all diagonals intersect at right angles		*1 mark*
e	the length diagonal		*1 mark*

Note to Parent

This question covers several aspects of shape, including congruence (when two or more shapes are exactly alike), symmetry and angle. In addition, children need to measure the diagonals and, at this level, approximate to the nearest half a centimetre in order to find which shapes are congruent. As your child's maths skills and knowledge increase, she or he will be expected to develop further precision in shape recognition and their associated properties (such as recognising that the shorter diagonal is bisected at a right angle by the other) and in measurement.

Total 10 marks

31	a	5.0 m	*1 mark*
	b	Check that your child has drawn 4.9 m correctly on the graph	*1 mark*
	c	Tuesday	*1 mark*
	d	Monday and Wednesday	*1 mark*
	e	5·3 – 4·7 = 0·6	*1 mark*

Note to Parent

This question tests your child's ability to interpret information presented in the form of a graph. The range (part **e**) is the difference between the largest and smallest values.

Total 5 marks

32

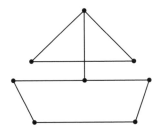

Award four marks if each step is correct; deduct a mark for each mistake   4 marks

Note to Parent

You may find the following explanations helpful:

multiple: 18 is a multiple of 6 because it is in the 6 times table, 6 x 3 = 18;

factor: 6 is a factor of 18 because 6 will divide into 18;

square number: this is the answer obtained by multiplying a number by itself, for example 6 x 6 = 36, so 36 is the square number of 6

square root: this is the number being multiplied by itself to give a square number, for example 6 is the square root of 36

prime number: a prime number has no factors other than itself and 1. No other whole number will divide into it. The first few prime numbers are: 2, 3, 5, 7, 11 and 13.

Encourage your child to recall all he or she knows about a number, for example, 16 is a multiple of 2, 4 and 8, it is a square number and a factor of 32.

Total 4 marks

33 a 140 + 250 + 140 + 250 = 780 cm *1 mark*
   b 8 metres *1 mark*
   c 12 × 2.5 = 30 cm *1 mark*

Note to Parent

In part **a** the perimeter of the shape is calculated. You could draw shapes on centimetre squared paper to give your child further practice.

Total 3 marks

34 a £14.73 *1 mark*
   b Arrow *1 mark*
   c £9.82 *1 mark*

Note to Parent

The context lends itself to other questions, for example 'How much does the petrol cost for our car each week?' or other things bought in standard sizes, such as washing powder.

Total 3 marks

35 a £11.50 per week, giving £46 per month *1 mark*
   b £1 *1 mark*
   c Badminton £4.05 Squash £2.25
      Aerobics £1.44 Spectators 36p *1 mark each*

Note to Parent

This question involves a variety of number operations – addition, multiplication and division. To help your child with the percentage question, it may be useful for you to talk about 10% of £1.00 being 10p.

Total 6 marks

36 a

Shape	Perimeter
A	12 cm
B	12 cm
C	10 cm
D	12 cm
E	12 cm

5 marks

   b Shapes A, B and E will all fold to make an open box *1 mark*

Note to Parent

This question looks at both perimeter and nets of cubes. Children can investigate nets of cubes and cuboids by opening flat empty cereal boxes and other types of cardboard packaging. Visualising solids made from flat nets will be easier for children after these practical experiences.

Total 6 marks

37 a   Cuboid   Prism

Edge	Parallel to
a	c
b	d, g, h
f	e

Edge	Parallel to
a	g, f
b	c
e	d

Award three marks for each correctly completed shape   *6 marks*

b   pentagon and rectangle   *1 mark*

Note to Parent

This question concerns solid shapes and their properties. Sets of parallel lines can be observed in most regular solid shapes and the hexagonal prism together with the cuboid are no exception to this. Children can be introduced to parallel lines through both drawing and the handling of solid containers, such as cereal boxes etc.

Total 7 marks

38 a   186   *1 mark*
      b   46   *1 mark*
      c   465   *1 mark*
      d   396   *1 mark*

Note to Parent

To calculate fractions of whole numbers, your child needs to use division, for example, half of 230 is 230 divided by two.

Total 4 marks

39 a   £37.50   *1 mark*
      b   £31.35   *1 mark*
      c   £6.15   *1 mark*
      d   £6.75   *1 mark*

Note to Parent

Make up other question for your child to practise their arithmetic with. Shopping catalogues and newspaper advertisements are a useful source of information. This question gives an indication of the difficulty to be experienced.

Total 4 marks

40 a   x + y + y + x + z   or   2x + 2y + z   *1 mark*
      b   2 + 4 + 4 + 2 + 6   or   2 × 2 + 2 × 4 + 6 = 18 cm   *1 mark*

Note to Parent

Creating a simple formula and substituting numbers is a skill that needs practising.

Total 2 marks

MARKING GRID

LEVEL 3 **Pages 1–6**

Question	Marks available	Marks scored
1	2	
2	5	
3	9	
4	3	
5	1	
6	3	
7	3	
8	3	
9	2	
10	6	
Total	**37**	

LEVEL 4 **Pages 7–20**

Question	Marks available	Marks scored
11	5	
12	5	
13	4	
14	5	
15	4	
16	5	
17	10	
18	6	
19	7	
20	2	
21	7	
22	3	
23	4	
24	3	
25	7	
Total	**77**	

LEVEL 5 **Pages 21–34**

Question	Marks available	Marks scored
26	4	
27	2	
28	2	
29	5	
30	10	
31	5	
32	4	
33	3	
34	3	
35	6	
36	6	
37	7	
38	4	
39	4	
40	2	
Total	**67**	